and the ducks

Lydia and her mum went for a picnic.

They sat by the river.

Lydia wanted to feed the ducks.

She threw some bread to a duck.

The duck called his friends.

Ducks came from everywhere.

'Look at all the ducks,' said Lydia.

Some ducks came out of the water...

. . . to eat out of Lydia's hand.

A sparrow sat on Lydia's head.

The ducks had eaten all the bread.

'Oh no!' said Lydia.

'The ducks have eaten our lunch.'

'Never mind,' said Mum.
'We'll go home for lunch.'

LYDIA

at the shops

Lydia and her mum made shopping lists.

They got into the car and ...

...drove to the supermarket.

Lydia sat in the trolley.

They looked at their lists.

They put things in the trolley.

There was a long queue.

A man put the shopping in a box.

The box was very heavy.

They emptied the box.

'Where did these come from?' said Mum.

'They're mine,' said Lydia.

'They were on my shopping list.'

and her garden

It was raining.
Lydia was sad.

She wanted to play outside.

'We can make a garden inside,' said Mum.

She put some blotting paper in a dish.

She sprinkled on some seeds and water.

Lydia made it look like a garden.

She watered the garden every day.

The cress seeds grew and grew.

Soon the cress was ready to eat.

Mum cut some cress.
'I'm hungry', said Lydia.

Mum made cheese and cress sandwiches.

Lydia took a big bite.

'Oh! I don't like cress!' said Lydia.